Time for Bed

TED 1

This book belongs to:

....

Down on the farm
It's the end of the day.

The **cat** and her **kittens**

Snuggle down in the hay.

There is one final job

Tractor Ted has to do...

He checks
all the animals,

Big...

...and small too.

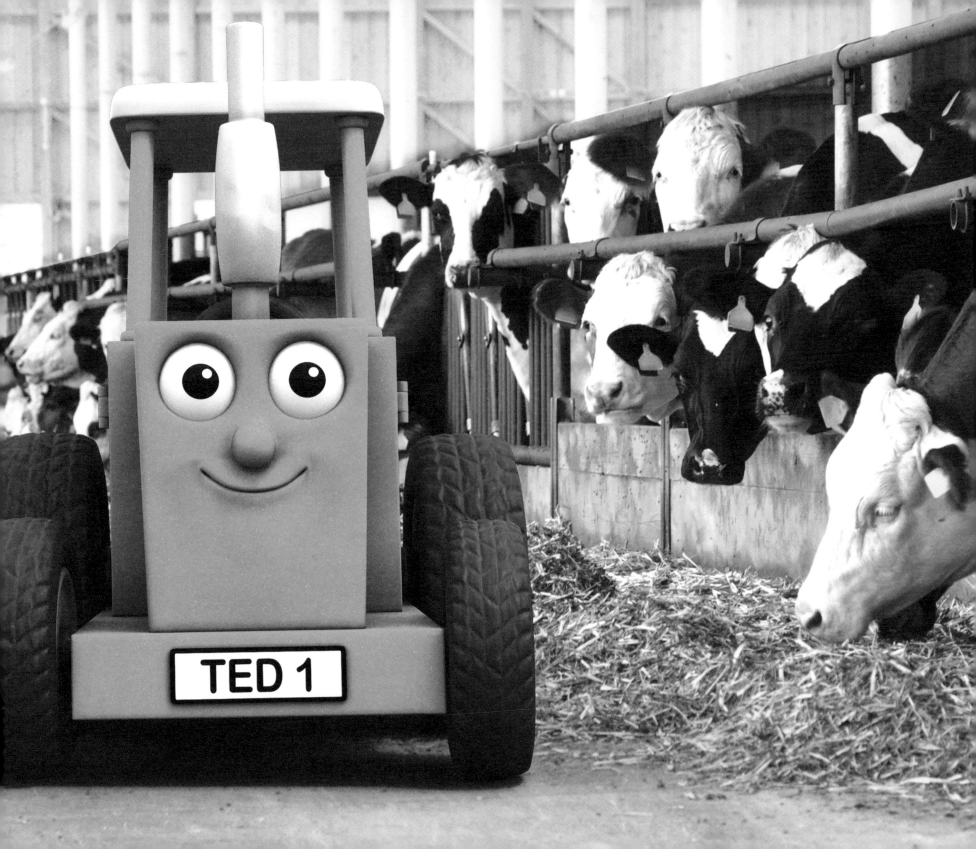

The **COWS** are inside...
with some
silage to eat.
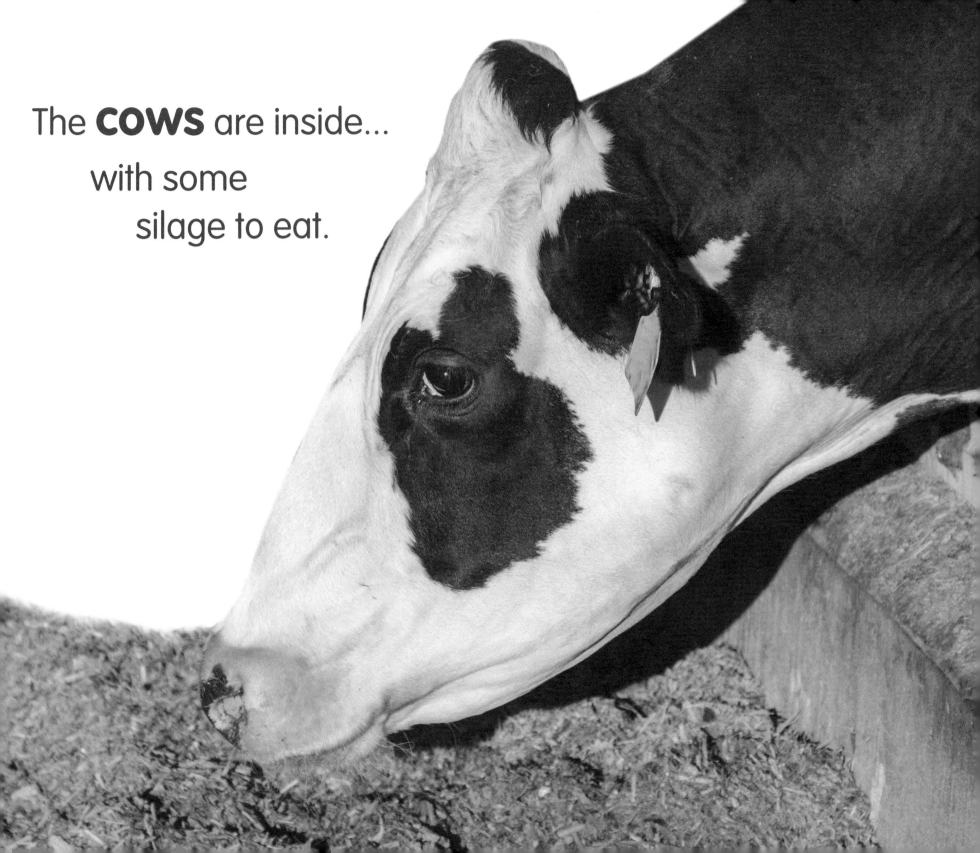

The **lambs** are all cosy.

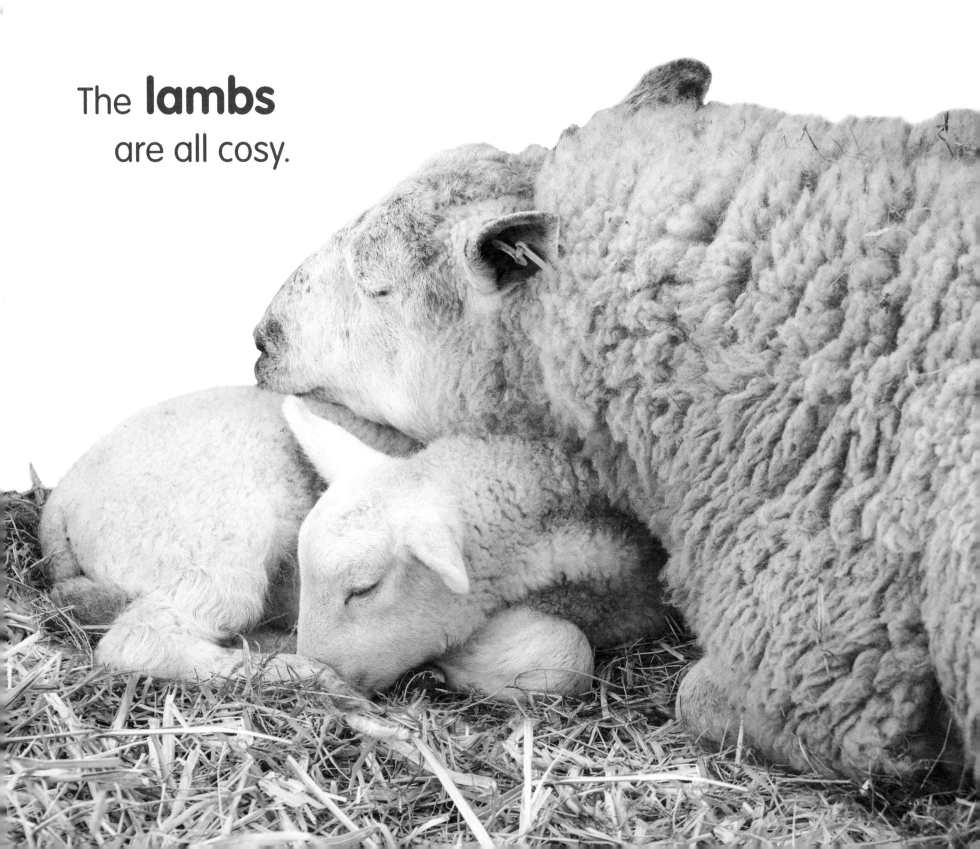

Don't they look sweet!

Here are the tractors

TED 1

With wheels washed clean.

Of the mud
and the muck

From the fields
where they've been.

The **horses** are happily munching their hay.

TED 1

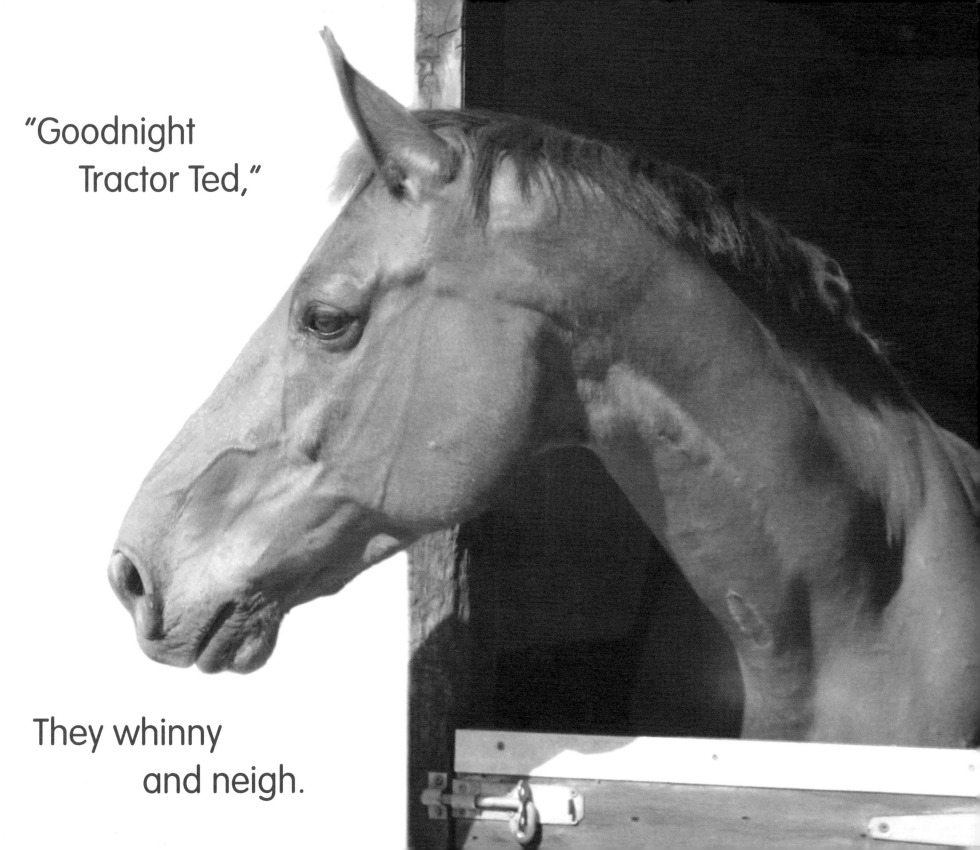

"Goodnight
    Tractor Ted,"

They whinny
    and neigh.

"Oink Oink,"
say the **piglets**.

There should be one more!

Oh look!
There it is,

Hiding under the straw.

A good night's sleep
Is so important for you.

Come on now Midge,
It's our bedtime too.

"Goodnight to you all.
Toot, toot," he says.

As Tractor Ted
Drives into his shed.

As Tractor Ted
Drives into his shed.

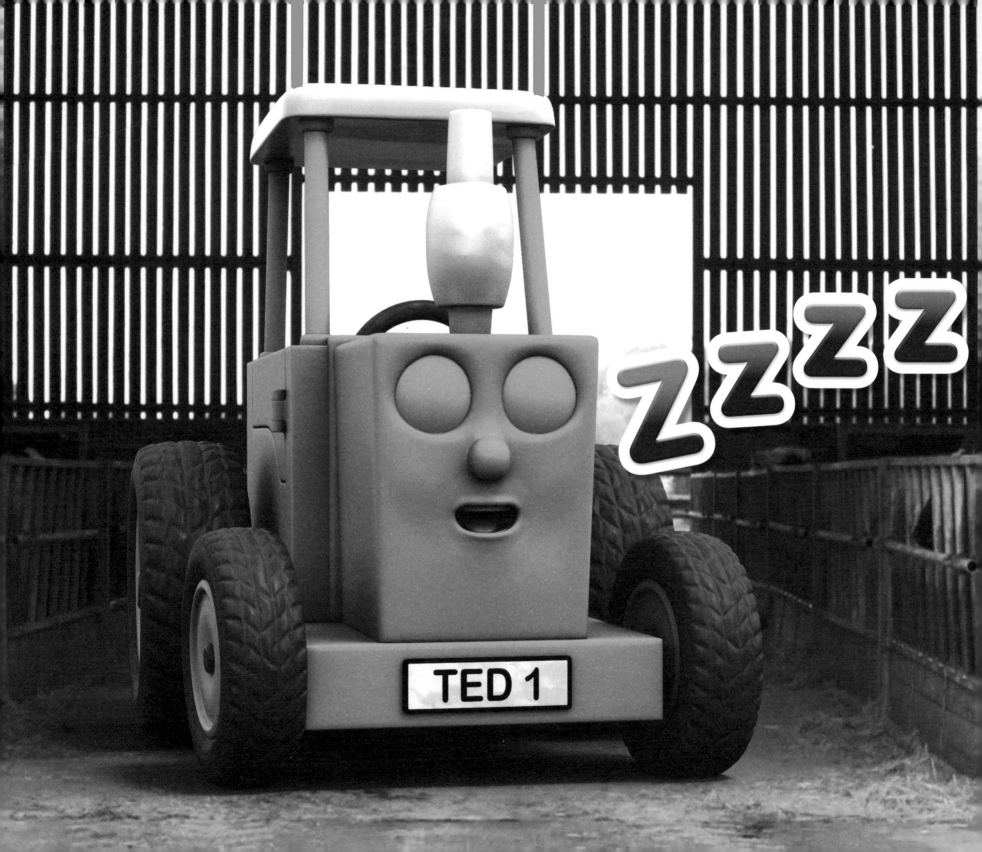